His Love Is

A Flourish Bible Study Journal

by

Mindy Kiker and Jenny Kochert

Women *growing* in God's Word

Welcome,

We are delighted that you are here. Your presence with us signals a season of refreshing, a time to dig into the Bible and hear God speak.

You hold in your hands a **Flourish Bible Study Journal** which guides you to spend time in the Word, filling your mind and heart with His truth. When you discover that He is good and that you are called, you can walk fearlessly into the future.

We have prayed that you would become *"like an olive tree flourishing in the house of God . . . trusting in God's unfailing love for ever and ever."* Psalm 52:8

Whatever the circumstances of your life right now, God's Word is waiting to meet you exactly where you are with the help that you need to take the next step.

We all have seasons where we drift away from Jesus and His Word. It is easy to get busy with the daily cares of life or to become embroiled in a fiery trial. This Bible Study Journal invites you to create a quiet space to cultivate confidence in your life right now. We pray that as you posture yourself to hear, you will receive the Word that you need to step forward into the fulfillment of the promises that God has spoken.

You are going to be amazed at what you discover as you pursue the daily practices of the DECLARE Bible Study Approach. One friend likens it to *"Holy Spirit sunglasses"* that allow you to see through the surface into the deep waters: *"I've been able to see deeper into the Bible than I've ever done before. The Holy Spirit has used DECLARE to bring much more life into my Bible time."* With regular use, it will become your own personal method to dig into any part of the Bible with an expectation of opening the Word and hearing Jesus speak.

This **Flourish Bible Study Journal** has been created from our God-breathed desire to walk with you, to take the truth you explore in Scripture and see it activated in your life. Regular time with Jesus nourishes the seeds of hope with the soil of truth, the sunshine of companionship, and the water of prayer to ignite growth in your heart.

May the seeds planted in your life grow and bloom as you open the Bible and enjoy time in God's presence. We stand with you in expectation at how Jesus is going to show up in your life as you feast on His Word.

We want to share with you how to get the most out of your **Flourish Bible Study Journal.** Like most things in life, you get out what you put into it. Go the gym and watch others do the heavy lifting, and not much is going to happen to your muscles -- but grab a set of dumbbells, start reaching for the sky, and you'll see results! Choosing to embark on a study with us is a great first step to strengthening your spiritual muscles. And now for some hot tips on how to start reaching for the sky:

1. **Fight for your fifteen**. Set aside at least 15 minutes each day to dig in. *"Commit to the Lord whatever you do, and he will establish your plans."* *(Proverbs 15:3)* Five days each week, you'll work through a stage of the DECLARE Bible Study Approach focusing on the declaration scripture for that week. If you have more time, there are additional ideas for digging into the Word further, and there is also an optional daily reading plan. We have designed the study with our less-is-more approach to Bible study which goes deep into a small portion of scripture using all our senses to explore God's Word.

2. **Get curious about the Word**. What does the Word say about your situation? What does it say about God himself? What does it say about your family? What does it way about the future? As you learn more about the Bible, how to study it, and how to dig deeper, you will become hungry to get into the Bible and to know it well.

3. **Get to Know Jesus**. Jesus is the Word personified. He embodies everything God desires to reveal to us. John tells us that *"the Word became flesh and dwelt among us." (John 1:14)* That's Jesus! His life of love and obedience crushed the power of death. By getting to know Him, we come to understand the whole Bible in terms of God's plan to rescue all of humanity – this includes you and me, right here, right now, today!

4. **Seek for a personal word**. When trying to gain understanding, we look for answers in several places. You may seek counsel with trusted leaders in your life. It is good to seek wisdom in a multitude of counsel, but then you must draw away to a quiet place and seek God yourself. We usually say, *"Father, I have sought much advice, and now I want to know what You have to say about this situation."* When we pursue God in this way, and the inevitable storms come, the Word that God has spoken will hold us like an anchor to the Rock.

This is how you can flourish in faith, family and life. You dig into the Word. You fasten your gaze on the person of Jesus. You wait until you receive a personal word. The **DECLARE Bible Study Approach** is the key to bringing all these elements together. This less-is-more approach guides you to dig into the Bible and hear Jesus speak.

When we press into God's Word and hear His voice, we gain confidence that He will never fail us. God may be later than expected. He may not answer like we imagined, but He knows what we need. One of the characteristics of God is that He loves multiplication. This is good news! **When pursuing God, you get out MORE than you put into it.** Psalm 34:4 says, *"God met me more than halfway."* *(MSG)* We're thrilled that you're here, digging in with us.

Table of Contents

Reading Plan & Weekly Scripture Declaration

Week 1   Reading Plan – Ruth Chapter 1

Week 1 Declaration – Psalm 86:15

"But you, O Lord, are a God of compassion and mercy, slow to get angry and filled with unfailing love and faithfulness" (NLT)

Week 2:   Reading Plan – Ruth Chapter 2

Week 2 Declaration – Romans 8:38

"And I am convinced that nothing can ever separate us from God's love. Neither death nor life, neither angels nor demons, neither our fears for today nor our worries about tomorrow—not even the powers of hell can separate us from God's love" Romans 8:38 (NLT)

Week 3:   Reading Plan – Ruth Chapter 3

Week 3 Declaration – Ruth 1:16

"But Ruth replied, 'Don't urge me to leave you or to turn back from you. Where you go I will go, and where you stay I will stay. Your people will be my people and your God my God' " Ruth 1:16 (NIV)

Week 4:   Reading Plan – Ruth Chapter 4

Week 4 Declaration – 1 John 4:10

"This is real love—not that we loved God, but that he loved us and sent his Son as a sacrifice to take away our sins" (NLT)

Declare Bible Study Approach

"We know that the Son of God has come and has given us understanding, so that we may know him who is true...."

1 John 5:20

The Declare Bible Study Approach equips us to dig deeper into a passage of scripture in order to know God's Word intimately and apply it to our lives. *(1 Corinthians 2:10-15)* When His Word is activated in our midst, new life is released, and we will begin to flourish where we are planted.

Preparation: Engage

Whenever you have time to dig into the Word, it is important to engage by tuning your ears and heart to God's voice. Take just a few minutes to pray through the following items:

Toss: Throw your cares on God. Let Him bear your burdens. *Psalm 55:22*
Catch: Receive the peace that surpasses all understanding. *Philippians 4:7*
Invite: Take every thought captive. Invite clarity and focus. Refuse confusion, distraction, or double-mindedness. *2 Corinthians 10:5*
Open: Ask God if you have turned away or closed your heart to anyone. Release the offense, open your heart, and give the situation into God's care. *Psalm 139:23*
Expect: Tell God that you are looking forward to hearing from Him. Let the excitement of time in His presence build expectation in your heart. *Habakkuk 2:1*

Declare Practice: Read & Write

Start with a verse or short passage that you want to explore further:

- Read the scripture slowly once or twice, even out loud if you are able.
- Write the scripture in your journal, including verses before and after.
- Read the entire chapter for context.
- Read the passage in another translation.

Declare Practice: Investigate

Once you have read the scripture and corresponding chapter, there are several options that you can use to look deeper into the meditation Scripture. Investigate as little or as much as time allows. Online resources like BibleGateway.com or BlueLetterBible.org will help:

- Highlight the words in the meditation verse you want to research more. Do a word study to gain greater insight into the passage.
- Read correlating verses, also called cross references. Reading cross references will help you better understand a verse, word, or principle.
- Read a commentary.

Declare Practice: Imagine

Read the meditation verse, and insert yourself in the story. Use your imagination to be present in the scene. Ask yourself the following questions:

- When and where is this taking place?
- Who is speaking? About what? Why?
- What are the characteristics of God as shown through this scripture or chapter?
- What are the promises of God as shown through this scripture or chapter?

Declare Practice: Listen

Invite the Words of Scripture and the Words of God to speak personally into your mind and heart. You can ask these questions:

- How do these verses apply to me?
- Is there anything that I need to receive or surrender in my life?
- Lord, how I can apply your Word to the frustrations, disappointments, fears, or hurts in my life?

Listening can be pursued for several days, and in fact, God will probably speak unexpectedly at random times of day or night as His revelation is released to you.

Declare Practice: DECLARE

Write out a declaration of what you have received as you meditated on the Word. This can be a statement of God's promise to you, an affirmation of the healing that He has given you, or a proclamation of a truth that has become real to you. A declaration can include Scripture or your own words, or some of each.

Let's Begin...

Love can be confusing. This powerful force is responsible for much of the pleasure and pain of life. To love is to open a doorway to the joy of belonging but also to the agony of betrayal or loss. If you do not love, you will not hurt, nor will you truly be alive. At times, this deep urge that God has written into our hearts for connection and intimacy with others can feel like a trap or a quandary.

When we are not convinced that God loves us, we either give up or we become overzealous, determined to earn His affection with our hard work. But strenuous spiritual disciplines are not the key to receiving His love. Believe it or not, He likes you just as you are. He's not waiting for you to improve yourself. God enjoys your company.

Our desire to love and to be loved is such a powerful draw in our lives. Sadly, we are simply too broken in our humanity to be able to love well, and so we set about on an impossible mission. Our determination to find love and belonging, meaning and joy in our most intimate relationships cannot be fulfilled without an intermediary.

Enter God, stage right.

Our Creator designed a love-sized space in our hearts as a beacon to draw us to Him. Although He knows that we will try to fill it with false lovers and counterfeit affections, He waits patiently for these substitutes to fail because He knows that they will not satisfy for long. He stands close by, ready to rush in with His never failing, never ending love.

God is patient, knowing that it will be a life-long process of responding to His whisper. During the course of this study, we will examine four areas of growth as we approach God's heart and begin to experience the abundant love that He longs to lavish upon us.

Time and time again throughout our journey toward restoration, each of us responds to God by acknowledging, believing, surrendering, and receiving His love:

1. **Acknowledging God's Love**
   Most of us approach our relationship with God initially through head knowledge of His love, but it has not yet got down into our hearts where it becomes an **unchanging** *force that we can count on to sustain us in the trials of life.*

2. **Believing God's Love**
   When God's love moves from our head to our heart, we believe with our whole being in the **unwavering** *strength of His steadfast dedication. We no longer doubt that we are secure in His love.*

3. **Surrendering to God's Love**
   When the reality of His love moves from our head to our heart, we desire to surrender to this God who is trustworthy, kind, and loyal. His **unfailing** *love invites us to yield completely to Him as our Lord and our Friend.*

4. **Receiving God's Love**
   The surrendered heart is positioned to receive God's **unconditional** *love that will never fail us. Jehovah God redeems us and restores us to His heart. Jesus becomes our peace, our refuge, and deepest joy.*

We are delighted to open the story of Ruth as a guide to appropriating the redeeming power of God's love in our lives. We encounter the family of Elimelech and Naomi with their two sons sometime after the period of the judges (1375–1050 B.C.) in a dark time when the people of Israel live for themselves rather than in dedication to God.

As we ponder the lives of Naomi, Boaz, and Ruth, we discover a story of God's redeeming love, an invitation to cleave to His heart, embraced by the outstretched hands of Jesus Christ.

The four Declaration Verses and weekly devotionals will encourage you to open yourself to God's love and receive a divine impartation which can satisfy your yearning heart. We believe you will discover a love story written especially for you.

Week One

God's Love is Unchanging

DECLARATION VERSE

"But you, O Lord, are a God of compassion and mercy, slow to get angry and filled with unfailing love and faithfulness" Psalm 86:15 (NLT)

As you enter your time of Bible Study this week, take a moment to "engage" by tuning your ears and heart to God's voice.

Toss: Throw your cares on God. Let Him bear your burdens. *Psalm 55:22*
Catch: Receive the peace that surpasses all understanding. *Philippians 4:7*
Invite: Take every thought captive. Invite clarity and focus. Refuse confusion, distraction, or double-mindedness. *2 Corinthians 10:5*
Open: Ask God if you have turned away or closed your heart to anyone. Release the offense, open your heart, and give the situation into God's care. *Psalm 139:23*
Expect: Tell God that you are looking forward to hearing from Him. Let the excitement of time in His presence build expectation in your heart. *Habakkuk 2:1*

The King Whispers your Name

My mom asked me an important question, "Mindy, do you believe that your daddy and I love you unconditionally?"

I replied, "Oh no, not at all. (I was a teenager at the time – insert eyes rolling here.) Do you really expect me to believe that you love me just as much when I rebel as when I obey? No way. You cannot convince me that I am as loveable when I'm angry, selfish, or disagreeable as when I'm an angel."

She looked concerned and pressed further, "Do you believe that God loves you unconditionally?"

I pondered for a moment and replied honestly, "I know it here (pointing to my head). I know that Jesus loves me because the Bible tells me so, but I do not know it here (pointing to my heart)."

My mother breathed a seemingly innocent prayer that day: "God, move it from her head to her heart." Little did we know that simple request would unlock a chain of events that would significantly alter my life.

Does God love me?

God's love is alluring yet mysterious. Everything in this fallen world is designed to make us doubt His goodness and question His intentions. Instead of trusting in Him, we grasp for little gods, temporary comforts, relationships, and reassurances that we can hold in our hands, hear with our ears, or taste with our mouths.

When life's journey takes an unexpected turn, especially one that involves trouble or suffering, we cry out in desperation, accusing God of abandoning us. And if we are not careful, we are tempted to think that He does not care, He does not see, He does not hear.

Naomi Changes Her Name

We find that Naomi's life has taken an unexpected turn for the worse in Ruth chapter one. She finds herself in a foreign land, widowed by the death of her husband and then abandoned completely by the demise of her two sons. Her life is ruined. In those times, a woman without a husband and sons has nothing. Naomi's future is dark indeed; we can understand why she might doubt God's love for her. Indeed we see that she blames God for her misfortune. When she returns bereft to her homeland in Judah, she reveals her despair by changing her name:

> " 'Don't call me Naomi,' she told them. 'Call me Mara, because the
> Almighty has made my life very bitter. I went away full, but the Lord has
> brought me back empty. Why call me Naomi? The Lord has afflicted me;
> the Almighty has brought misfortune upon me.' "
> (Ruth 1:20-21, NIV)

Naomi accuses the Almighty for her misfortune. Her mind unsupported by a believing heart is unable to remain steadfast when storms rage. Fortunately, Mara acknowledges her despair and hopelessness. Many of us do not. We slip away from the strong arms of our Father God and separate ourselves from His love. Mara calls it like it is, but when we fail to name our grief, our passion for God cools. When we doubt His unchanging love, we slip slowly into apathy and drift away from His protective embrace.

Is His Love Unchanging?

What if Naomi had not believed? Might she have lived out her days as Mara? Our Declaration Verse proposes statements about God's character that may be difficult to believe when we are caught up in apathy, bitterness, or doubt. Let me provide an example of how we in our skepticism might be tempted to read this verse:

> But you, O Lord, are a God of compassion (*Is He really?*) and mercy
> (*Then why is there so much suffering?*), slow to get angry (*You're kidding,
> right?*) filled with unfailing love (*Tough love, maybe*) and faithfulness
> (*Then why do I feel so neglected?*). (Psalm 86:15, NIV, *with added
> commentary interspersed*)

The lament and longing of Psalm 86 sounds similar to the voice of Mara. David expresses his human frailty, and yet he confidently declares the unshakable nature of his God: *"You, Lord, are forgiving and good, abounding in love to all who call to you."* (verse 5) Love is the foundation of all, the greatest commandment (Matthew 22:40). It is unchanging. His Love is. Everything.

God Restores Naomi
Although Naomi tries on the name Mara, it does not hold. The Lord whispers her true name. He stops at nothing to draw each of His daughters close to His heart. God comes near to the brokenhearted, meets us in our anguish, and reveals that His love is indeed an unchanging and unmovable foundation for our lives. When we respond to Him, love moves from our head to our heart, and we are positioned to believe. His love ignites a steadfast hope in our hearts that does not falter, even in the midst of suffering.

Mara believes and discovers that the Almighty is indeed good. He is a Friend, not an enemy. His intentions toward Naomi are kind. Never does He falter in His promise to draw her forward into a future full of hope and promise. Unfortunately, when we possess only a superficial knowledge of God's love, we struggle to draw our gaze away from the immediate circumstances to see the bigger picture of Jehovah Jireh, our provider, who works out everything for our benefit.

Mara overcomes her disappointment in a seemingly faithless God, wooed by His love. She lets go of bitterness and returns to her true identity as Naomi or "pleasantness." She realizes that His love has sustained her until she finally perceives what He has intended from the beginning: to graft her daughter-in-law into an esteemed family line. Bitterness turns to honey on her tongue. Could she have imagined such an honor as a childless widow starving in a foreign land? Never. That is our God.

Our prayer for you during this study is that God draws you closer into His embrace. As you step into your love story, and fully inhabit your journey of restoration, may you respond to Jehovah God by receiving His deep affection for you. He desires to be the compassionate, merciful, kind, unfailing and faithful love of your life. Listen as the King whispers your name, "Come away with Me, My love."

God's Love is Unchanging: Read & Write

Declaration Verse:

"But you, O Lord, are a God of compassion and mercy, slow to get angry and filled with unfailing love and faithfulness" Psalm 86:15 (NLT)

[   ] Read Psalm 86:15 slowly once or twice, even out loud if you are able.

[ ] Write Psalm 86:14-16 in the space below*Feel free to get creative!*

[ ] Read Psalm Chapter 86 for context. Write out a few observations:

[ ] Read Psalm 86:15 in another Bible translation. Do you notice any differences?

Write your observations:

Digging Deeper: The Book of Ruth

[ ] Read Ruth Chapter 1

[ ] Write any verses that stand out to you as you read the chapter.

God's Love is Unchanging: Investigate

Declaration Verse: Psalm 86:15

Today we begin looking deeper into the Declaration Verse. Investigate as little or as much as time allows. Online resources like BibleGateway.com or BlueLetterBible.org will help you during your investigation.

[ ] Conduct a Word Study: Part One

Read the Declaration Verse or the entire chapter if you have more time. Spend a few minutes highlighting any words you want to research more.

Write these words below:

[ ] Conduct a Word Study: Part Two

Using BlueLetterBible.org or another online resource, choose a word you selected above to conduct your word study. This is as simple as looking up the original Greek or Hebrew word, reading the definitions of that word, and looking at how it is used in other verses in the Bible.

Record the results of your word study here:

[ ] Read any of the following cross references for Psalm 86:15:

    Isaiah 63:7
    Jonah 4:2
    Psalm 85:10-13

Reading cross references will help you better understand a verse, word, or principle.

What did you discover? Write your insights:

[ ] Read a commentary. A commentary is a collection of explanatory notes that a Bible scholar has written about passages of scripture. Write any observations, quotes, or notes:

Digging Deeper: The Book of Ruth

[ ] Refresh your memory of Ruth Chapter 1

[ ] Investigate

Highlight a couple key words that stand out to you in the chapter you read. Using BlueLetterBible.org look up the Greek or Hebrew word and definition of one of those words.

Write your findings below:

[ ] Write down any general thoughts or questions you have as you read the chapter today.

God's Love is Unchanging: Imagine

Declaration Verse: Psalm 86:15

Remember to take a moment to "engage" as you prepare to listen: toss, catch, invite, open, expect. Invite the Words of Scripture and the Words of God to speak personally into your mind and heart.

[ ] Read Psalm 86:15

You may want to scout around in your Bible for any notes or perhaps an introduction to this book of the Bible. When using your imagination, it helps to keep in mind the context of the chapter and book that you're in. Insert yourself in the story as you ponder the following questions. Use your imagination and all your senses to be present in the scene.

[ ] When and where is this taking place? What do you imagine you might see, hear, touch, taste, or smell?

[ ] Who is speaking or writing? Whom are they addressing? Others? God? Themselves?

[ ] What are they speaking or writing about? What is their purpose?

[ ] What are the characteristics of God as shown through the Declaration Verse or chapter?

Is He steadfast, faithful, just, trustworthy, nurturing, kind, gentle, or strong? What do you see revealed about His nature in this passage of Scripture?

[ ] What are the promises of God as shown through the Declaration Verse or chapter?

Write any observations, key words, or questions you have as you ponder the Declaration Verse. If you have time, you may want to do another word study.

Digging Deeper: The Book of Ruth

[ ] Refresh your memory of Ruth Chapter 1

[ ] Imagine

You may want flip back to the beginning of Ruth in your Bible to read the introduction. Or use an online resource. Insert yourself in the story as you ponder the following questions.

When and where is this taking place? Who is speaking? What is happening?

[ ] Write down any general thoughts or questions you have as you read the chapter today.

God's Love is Unchanging: Listen

Declaration Verse: Psalm 86:15

Remember to take a moment to "engage" as you prepare to listen: toss, catch, invite, open, expect. Invite the Words of Scripture and the Words of God to speak personally into your mind and heart. Remember that God's voice will never accuse you. He may bring gentle conviction, and that can cause some grief, but God always brings hope.

Listening can be pursued for several days, and in fact, God will probably speak unexpectedly at random times of day or night as His revelation is released to you. Ask these questions as you listen to God's voice:

[ ] How does the Declaration Verse apply to me?

[ ] Ponder and pray: how I can apply these truths to the frustrations, disappointments, fears, or hurts in my life? Is there anything I need to surrender or receive in my life?

Digging Deeper: The Book of Ruth

[ ] Refresh your memory of Ruth Chapter 1

[ ] Listen

Ask yourself: how does what I have read so far in Ruth Chapter 1 apply to me? Does God want to speak to my heart today through this story?

God's Love is Unchanging: Declare

Declaration Verse: Psalm 86:15

Write out a declaration of what you have received as you meditated on the Word. This can be a statement of God's promise to you, an affirmation of the healing that He has given you, or a proclamation of a truth that has become real to you. A declaration can include Scripture or your own words, or some of each.

Reflect upon your week

Write out Psalm 86:15 by hand if you memorized it, or summarize the Declaration Verse in your own words below.

Spend a few minutes documenting your insights, "a-ha" moments, and revelations from this week of digging into the Bible.

Digging Deeper: The Book of Ruth

[ ] Refresh your memory of Ruth Chapter 1

[ ] Spend a few minutes documenting your insights, "a-ha" moments, and
    revelations from this week of digging into Ruth.

Week One: Discussion Topics

We provide discussion topics if you want to gather with friends to enjoy this study together. You are welcome to use these points to help guide your conversation, or you can ponder these questions as a personal reflection. Even if you are not able to meet up with a girlfriend, you're invited to join us in our private Facebook Group at facebook.com/groups/flourishgathering/

1) Do you have any thoughts or reactions to this week's devotional? Here are two passages from *The King Whispers Your Name* that may inspire an interesting conversation:

   "God's love is alluring yet mysterious. Everything in this fallen world is designed to make us doubt His goodness and question His intentions. Instead of trusting in Him, we grasp for little gods, temporary comforts, relationships, and reassurances that we can hold in our hands, hear with our ears, or taste with our mouths."

   "Although Naomi tries on the name Mara, it does not hold. The Lord whispers her true name. He stops at nothing to draw each of His daughters close to His heart. God comes near to the brokenhearted, meets us in our anguish, and reveals that His love is indeed an unchanging and unmovable foundation for our lives."

2) Was there a special insight you gained from the **Investigate** practice? Perhaps an interesting word study, cross reference, or commentary?

3) What happened when you used your **Imagination**? What did you discover about the context of this chapter or book of the Bible? If you had time, did you gain insight into the character or promises of God?

4) Did God speak something special that you would like to share as you **Listened**?
5) What is your **Declaration**? How can we pray for you in this regard?
6) How about the Ruth reading plan? Anything interesting there?
7) How can we support one another this week? Prayer requests? Praise reports?

Notes

Week Two

God's Love is Unwavering

DECLARATION VERSE

"And I am convinced that nothing can ever separate us from God's love. Neither death nor life, neither angels nor demons, neither our fears for today nor our worries about tomorrow—not even the powers of hell can separate us from God's love." Romans 8:38 (NLT)

As you enter your time of Bible Study this week, take a moment to "engage" by tuning your ears and heart to God's voice.

Toss: Throw your cares on God. Let Him bear your burdens. *Psalm 55:22*
Catch: Receive the peace that surpasses all understanding. *Philippians 4:7*
Invite: Take every thought captive. Invite clarity and focus. Refuse confusion, distraction, or double-mindedness. *2 Corinthians 10:5*
Open: Ask God if you have turned away or closed your heart to anyone. Release the offense, open your heart, and give the situation into God's care. *Psalm 139:23*
Expect: Tell God that you are looking forward to hearing from Him. Let the excitement of time in His presence build expectation in your heart. *Habakkuk 2:1*

Nothing Can Ever Separate Us

How do we allow God's love to permeate our lives, to fill us up to overflowing with a steadfast confidence in His goodness? How can we become convinced that He is faithful and kind? Many of us know the theory of God's love, but we lack certainty in our hearts. How does His love make that journey from our head to our heart where it becomes a tangible, unwavering force in our lives?

It is not a single event that completes this move, but instead it is a life-long journey as we are drawn incrementally, year by year, circumstance by circumstance, closer to God's love for us. At times, we can point to specific experiences that strengthen our ability to trust Him with our hearts so that we do not merely acknowledge His love, but instead we believe His love.

How did God's love move from my head to my heart?

One season of significant growth in my life was initiated by my mom's prayer requesting that the knowledge of God's love move from my head to my heart. Caution! This is an important but risky request. Removing the barriers that keep God's love out of our hearts may involve a few bumps in the road. Soon after my mom prayed for me, I decided that I was finished with God. I requested to stop attending church, and determined that I did not want to follow Christ any longer.

As my parents frantically petitioned the Lord on my behalf, God impressed upon my mom, "This is My answer to your prayer."

"What?!" she responded incredulously, "What prayer was that? Can I take it back?"

She sensed His reply, "Remember when you prayed that Mindy would know with certainty that I love her unconditionally? Well, I'm in the process of answering your prayer in her life."

Jehovah God wanted me to know that there is nothing I can do to earn His love, and there is nothing I can do to lose it. He loves me because He is love. His nature is love. I thought I needed to perform for acceptance. The Lord wished to remove this barrier so I could know that my performance is of little consequence. He loves us because He is love, not because we are good enough to earn His love.

The best way for me to experience this was to turn away from Him so that He could prove that He never gives up on me; He never stops loving me, and my relationship with Him is based not on my goodness, but on His faithfulness. It took about a year and a half of wandering, trying to find meaning in the wisdom of the world, but eventually I returned to my first Love, at last convinced of His unwavering love for me.

I am convinced

In Romans chapter 8, Paul describes the importance of freeing our mind from fleshly desires, and instead learning to live in accordance to the Holy Spirit (verse 5). This shift moves us into a place of life and peace, positioned to trust in God's love. When we allow Holy Spirit to speak into our mind and heart, we see ourselves as insiders, not outsiders. We do not live as fearful slaves, but instead we are adopted as heirs in God's family, and our hearts cry out, "Abba, Father." (verse 15)

Finding life alongside the Spirit rather than the flesh, or sin nature, leads us into an intimate place of knowing God: *"The person without the Spirit does not accept the things that come from the Spirit of God but considers them foolishness, and cannot understand them because they are discerned only through the Spirit." (I Corinthians 2:14, NIV)*

When our mind knows and our heart responds to God, we are convinced that His love is not at all foolish. It is difficult to comprehend a love so true, so perfect and unfailing, yet with our heart connected to Holy Spirit, we are able to believe this outrageous claim:

> *I am convinced that nothing can ever separate us from God's love. Neither death nor life, neither angels nor demons, neither our fears for today nor our worries about tomorrow—not even the powers of hell can separate us from God's love. (Romans 8:38, NLT)*

Can this be true? When we feel the powers of hell attacking, we can respond without fear from a steadfast heart, shielded by faith which believes in a God who is able, in a sacred love that is unwavering.

God's love revealed through Boaz

Boaz did not have the advantage of reading Romans 8, and yet his life exemplifies a true and Godly love in the story of Ruth. He is the Kinsman Redeemer, positioned to rescue this young widow, a foreigner from Moab, to graft her into the royal family line of King David and Jesus Himself. This is a picture of our God who invites us to become His children, complete with an inheritance of the grandest proportions.

As I read Ruth chapter 2, a question arises, "How did she 'happen to go to the part of the field belonging to Boaz' to glean?" (verse 3) Why doesn't the account give God the credit? Surely He led her. My word study leaves me stunned. The verse is made up of two seemingly opposite Hebrew words paired together: "her 'accidental' (*miqreh*) gleaning on Boaz's field is actually an 'appointment' (one of the meanings of *qarah*)." This is no accident.

This is our God! His love is a powerful force that draws us into life, into redemption, into restoration. God's love makes an "appointment" for Ruth to "accidentally" find her way to her Kinsman Redeemer. What a picture of Jesus' unwavering love that draws us to His heart where we are made whole, and relieved of the suffering that threatens to destroy us.

The Father's pure, gentle, powerful love is too fantastic for our mind to grasp. We need Holy Spirit to come to the rescue: " 'What no eye has seen, what no ear has heard, and what no human mind has conceived' -- the things God has prepared for those who love him -- these are the things God has revealed to us by his Spirit." (1 Corinthians 2:9-10, NIV)

Your good Father wishes to reveal the love story He has prepared for you. You may not be able to conceive what He has ready and waiting, but your heart believes that it is available, and God has appointed for you to find it. May you "accidentally" find your way to the inheritance that Jehovah God has prepared in advance to provide exactly what you need right now. Today. Pure. Redeeming. Love.

God's Love in Unwavering: Read & Write

Declaration Verse:

"And I am convinced that nothing can ever separate us from God's love. Neither death nor life, neither angels nor demons, neither our fears for today nor our worries about tomorrow—not even the powers of hell can separate us from God's love." Romans 8:38

[ ] Read Romans 8:38 slowly once or twice, even out loud if you are able.

[ ] Write Romans 8:37-39 in the space below. *Feel free to get creative!*

[ ] Read Romans Chapter 8 for context. Write out a few observations:

[ ] Read Roman 8:38 in another Bible translation. Do you notice any differences?

Write your observations

Digging Deeper: The Book of Ruth

[ ] Read Ruth Chapter 2

[ ] Write any verses that stand out to you as you read the chapter.

God's Love is Unwavering: Investigate

Declaration Verse: Romans 8:38

Today we begin looking deeper into the Declaration Verse. Investigate as little or as much as time allows. Online resources like BibleGateway.com or BlueLetterBible.org will help you during your investigation.

[ ] Conduct a Word Study: Part One

Read the Declaration Verse or the entire chapter if you have more time. Spend a few minutes highlighting any words you want to research more.

Write these words below:

[ ] Conduct a Word Study: Part Two

Using BlueLetterBible.org or another online resource, choose a word you
selected above to conduct your word study. This is as simple as looking up the
original Greek or Hebrew word, reading the definitions of that word, and
looking at how it is used in other verses in the Bible.

Record the results of your word study here:

[ ] Read any of the following cross references for Romans 8:38:

Ephesians 3:14-21
Philippians 3:7-14
Romans 5:8

Reading cross references will help you better understand a verse, word, or principle.

What did you discover? Write your insights:

[ ] Read a commentary. A commentary is a collection of explanatory notes that a Bible scholar has written about passages of scripture. Write any observations, quotes, or notes:

Digging Deeper: The Book of Ruth

[ ] Refresh your memory of Ruth Chapter 2

[ ] Investigate

Highlight a couple key words that stand out to you in the chapter you read. Using BlueLetterBible.org look up the Greek or Hebrew word and definition of one of those words.

Write your findings below:

[ ] Write down any general thoughts or questions you have as you read the chapter today.

God's Love is Unwavering: Imagine

Declaration Verse: Romans 8:38

> *Remember to take a moment to "engage" as you prepare to listen: toss, catch, invite, open, expect. Invite the Words of Scripture and the Words of God to speak personally into your mind and heart.*

[ ] Read Romans 8:38

You may want to scout around in your Bible for any notes or perhaps an introduction to this book of the Bible. When using your imagination, it helps to keep in mind the context of the chapter and book that you're in. Insert yourself in the story as you ponder the following questions. Use your imagination and all your senses to be present in the scene.

[ ] When and where is this taking place? What do you imagine you might see, hear, touch, taste, or smell?

[ ] Who is speaking or writing? Whom are they addressing? Others? God? Themselves?

[ ] What are they speaking or writing about? What is their purpose?

[ ] What are the characteristics of God as shown through the Declaration Verse or chapter?

Is He steadfast, faithful, just, trustworthy, nurturing, kind, gentle, or strong? What do you see revealed about His nature in this passage of Scripture?

[ ] What are the promises of God as shown through the Declaration Verse or chapter?

Write any observations, key words, or questions you have as you ponder the Declaration Verse. If you have time, you may want to do another word study.

Digging Deeper: The Book of Ruth

[ ] Refresh your memory of Ruth Chapter 2

[ ] Imagine

You may want flip back to the beginning of Ruth in your Bible to read the introduction. Or use on online resource. Insert yourself in the story as you ponder the following questions.

When and where is this taking place? Who is speaking? What is happening?

God's Love is Unwavering: Listen

Declaration Verse: Romans 8:38

Remember to take a moment to "engage" as you prepare to listen: toss, catch, invite, open, expect. Invite the Words of Scripture and the Words of God to speak personally into your mind and heart. Remember that God's voice will never accuse you. He may bring gentle conviction, and that can cause some grief, but God always brings hope.

Listening can be pursued for several days, and in fact, God will probably speak unexpectedly at random times of day or night as His revelation is released to you. Ask these questions as you listen to God's voice:

[ ] How does the Declaration Verse apply to me?

[ ] Ponder and pray: how I can apply these truths to the frustrations, disappointments, fears, or hurts in my life? Is there anything I need to receive or surrender in my life?

Digging Deeper: The Book of Ruth

[ ] Refresh your memory of Ruth Chapter 2

[ ] Listen

Ask yourself: how does what I have read so far in Ruth Chapter 2 apply to me? Does God want to speak to my heart today through this story?

[ ] Write down any general thoughts or questions you have as you read the chapter today.

God's Love is Unwavering: Declare

Declaration Verse: Romans 8:38

Write out a declaration of what you have received as you meditated on the Word. This can be a statement of God's promise to you, an affirmation of the healing that He has given you, or a proclamation of a truth that has become real to you. A declaration can include Scripture or your own words, or some of each.

Reflect upon your week

Write out Romans 8:38 by hand if you memorized it, or summarize the Declaration Verse in your own words below.

Spend a few minutes documenting your insights, "a-ha" moments, and revelations from this week of digging into the Bible.

Digging Deeper: The Book of Ruth

[ ] Refresh your memory of Ruth Chapter 2

[ ] Spend a few minutes documenting your insights, "a-ha" moments, and revelations from this week of digging into Ruth.

Week Two: Discussion Topics

We provide discussion topics if you want to gather with friends to enjoy this study together. You are welcome to use these points to help guide your conversation, or you can ponder these questions as a personal reflection. Even if you are not able to meet up with a girlfriend, you're invited to join us in our private Facebook Group at facebook.com/groups/flourishgathering/

1) Do you have any thoughts or reactions to this week's devotional? Here are two passages from *Nothing Can Ever Separate Us* that may inspire an interesting conversation:

> *"Jehovah God wanted me to know that there is nothing I can do to earn His love, and there is nothing I can do to lose it. He loves me because He is love. His nature is love. I thought I needed to perform for acceptance. . . . He loves us because He is love, not because we are good enough to earn His love."*

> *"God's love is a powerful force that draws us into life, into redemption, into restoration. God's love makes an 'appointment' for Ruth to 'accidentally' find her way to her Kinsman Redeemer. What a picture of Jesus' unwavering love that draws us to His heart where we are made whole. . . ."*

2) Was there a special insight you gained from the **Investigate** practice? Perhaps an interesting word study, cross reference, or commentary?

3) What happened when you used your **Imagination**? What did you discover about the context of this chapter or book of the Bible? If you had time, did you gain insight into the character or promises of God?

4) Did God speak something special that you would like to share as you **Listened**?

5) What is your **Declaration**? How can we pray for you in this regard?

6) How about the Ruth reading plan? Anything interesting there?

7) How can we support one another this week? Prayer requests? Praise reports?

Notes

Week Three

God's Love is Unfailing

DECLARATION VERSE

"But Ruth replied, 'Don't urge me to leave you or to turn back from you. Where you go I will go, and where you stay I will stay. Your people will be my people and your God my God.' " Ruth 1:16 (NIV)

As you enter your time of Bible Study this week, take a moment to "engage" by tuning your ears and heart to God's voice.

Toss: Throw your cares on God. Let Him bear your burdens. *Psalm 55:22*
Catch: Receive the peace that surpasses all understanding. *Philippians 4:7*
Invite: Take every thought captive. Invite clarity and focus. Refuse confusion, distraction, or double-mindedness. *2 Corinthians 10:5*
Open: Ask God if you have turned away or closed your heart to anyone. Release the offense, open your heart, and give the situation into God's care. *Psalm 139:23*
Expect: Tell God that you are looking forward to hearing from Him. Let the excitement of time in His presence build expectation in your heart. *Habakkuk 2:1*

A Passionate Pursuit

We join the story of Ruth this week at a crucial crossroads. In Ruth 1:8 Naomi urges her daughters-in-law, Ruth and Orpah, to return to their respective families as they have been widowed by the death of Naomi's sons. She reviews their unfortunate situation, expressing her disappointment that she has nothing of value to offer her two sweet daughters. Ruth and Orpah clearly love their mother-in-law, as the text tells us they weep loudly and try to convince Naomi to let them accompany her. Emotions are high, and I can imagine the tense scene that day.

Naomi packs her few belongings and heads back home to the land of Judah. I envision her doing a power-walk of sorts, trying to get out of town as quickly as possible. Ruth and Orpah follow closely behind, listening to Naomi present the reasons they should not depart from their families and sacrifice everything familiar. She convinces Orpah to return home, yet Ruth makes a decision that changes the course of history:

> *At this they wept aloud again. Then Orpah kissed her mother-in-law goodbye,* **but Ruth clung to her.** *(Ruth 1:14, NIV)*

Your God will be my God

Ruth is a Moabite who married into Naomi's family. Moab was a pagan land that descended from a son of Lot through the incestuous relationship with his daughters. Moabites did not worship the God of Israel, yet after ten years of marriage Ruth must have become acquainted with the God Naomi worshipped.

When Naomi loses her husband and two sons, she hears that the Lord has visited her homeland of Judah and provided food for them. She decides to return to the place she can find provision. Ruth has to decide if she will leave her people, her comforts, her homeland, and her god, and instead place her trust in the God of Israel. Elizabeth Baxter says it well:

It must be a moment of decision for Ruth. Now she must declare whose god she worshipped. Something new had entered into the life of Ruth. She had heard, and her whole soul was penetrated with what she had heard, of the God of Israel. It was the tidings of **His faithfulness to His people** *which had influenced Naomi to return to her land. (Baxter Commentary on Ruth , emphasis added)*

Ruth is loyal. She loves Naomi and Naomi's God. She places her trust in the God of Israel, and as she clings to Naomi, she begins to surrender to the faithful love of the God of Abraham, Isaac, and Jacob. Ruth is determined, and while clinging to Naomi, she commemorates this decision stamped in history with one of the most famous lines in the entire Bible:

> *But Ruth replied, 'Don't urge me to leave you or to turn back from you. Where you go I will go, and where you stay I will stay. Your people will be my people and your God my God.' (Ruth 1:16, NIV)*

If her words were not clear enough, she further promises:
> *Where you die I will die, and there I will be buried. May the* LORD *deal with me, be it ever so severely, if even death separates you and me. (Ruth 1:17, NIV)*

When Naomi sees that Ruth is determined, they return together to Judah.

A Love that Pursues

I was fascinated to learn that the Hebrew word for cling, "dabaq" means "to hold fast or cleave to." It is the same word used in Genesis 2:24 when God instructs that a man should leave his family and cleave to his wife and become one flesh.

Difficult circumstances of life will either draw us away, like Orpah, or draw us toward God. It is the very nature of God to pursue us unfailingly with His love in all our circumstances of life.

Many years ago, I was in a very broken point in my life. One afternoon as I traveled back to my hometown, I felt in my heart that I needed to move from my home city back to the city where I had gone to college a couple years earlier. Although, I did not recognize the voice of God at the time, He clearly had spoken to my heart. At that moment, I had a choice to make, much like Ruth. I could stay with all the comforts of home and family, or I could follow the voice of God.

In the darkest moment of my life, God had neither forgotten nor forsaken me: *"For God has said, I will never leave you; I will never forsake you."* (*Hebrews 13:5, NIV*) He had spoken to me, and His faithfulness to pursue me with His love would ultimately change the course of my life forever.

Have you ever been at a crossroad of life with barely enough faith to believe? I wish to encourage you that God sees you, and He is wooing you with His love to come home to Him.

His Unfailing Love

I imagine the heart of God much like a faithful companion. God is willing to wait for us to return to Him, to surrender our hearts to His. God passionately loves you. He is love, yet He will never force His love upon you. He waits patiently for you to invite Him in, to cling to Him and surrender to Him.

But what if love has let you down? What if receiving God's love is frightening? When He asks us to surrender, all He is asking is for a willing heart. He does the rest. God's love meets us right where we are at in our faith walk. Yet, when we do surrender, even just a little part of our hearts, His love cleaves itself to us, and through the transforming power of His unfailing love, we begin to change from the inside out. God's Love is unfailing. It can be trusted, and it pursues us passionately, with such determination, that it compels us turn away from all that is safe and instead to surrender our way and our will and cling to God. The Psalmist says it beautifully:

> *Let the morning bring me word of your unfailing love, for I have put my trust in you. Show me the way I should go, for to you I entrust my life. (Psalm 143:8, NIV)*

Surrender is never easy, yet the rewards are great. As we continue to explore the story of Ruth, we see that the difficult, yet profound decision Ruth makes to surrender her very life over to the God of Israel, positions her to become part of the one of the greatest love stories ever told.

God's Love is Unfailing: Read & Write

Declaration Verse:

"But Ruth replied, 'Don't urge me to leave you or to turn back from you. Where you go I will go, and where you stay I will stay. Your people will be my people and your God my God.'" Ruth 1:16 (NIV)

[ ] Read Ruth 1:16 slowly once or twice, even out loud if you are able.

[ ] Write Ruth 1:14-17 in the space below. *Feel free to get creative!*

[ ] Read Ruth Chapter 1 for context. Write out a few observations:

[ ] Read Ruth 1:16 in another Bible translation. Do you notice any differences?

Write your observations

Digging Deeper: The Book of Ruth

[ ] Read Ruth Chapter 3

[ ] Write any verses that stand out to you as you read the chapter.

God's Love is Unfailing: Investigate

Declaration Verse: Ruth 1:16

Today we begin looking deeper into the Declaration Verse. Investigate as little or as much as time allows. Online resources like BibleGateway.com or BlueLetterBible.org will help you during your investigation.

[ ] Conduct a Word Study: Part One

Read the Declaration Verse or the entire chapter if you have more time. Spend a few minutes highlighting any words you want to research more.

    Write these words below:

[ ] Conduct a Word Study: Part Two

Using BlueLetterBible.org or another online resource, choose a word you selected above to conduct your word study. This is as simple as looking up the original Greek or Hebrew word, reading the definitions of that word, and looking at how it is used in other verses in the Bible.

Record the results of your word study here:

[ ] Read any of the following cross references for Ruth 1:16:

    2 Samuel 15:21
    2 Corinthians 6:18
    Psalm 45:10

    Reading cross references will help you better understand a verse, word, or principle.

    What did you discover? Write your insights:

[ ] Read a commentary. A commentary is a collection of explanatory notes that a Bible scholar has written about passages of scripture. Write any observations, quotes, or notes:

Digging Deeper: The Book of Ruth

[ ] Refresh your memory of Ruth Chapter 3

[ ] Investigate

Highlight a couple key words that stand out to you in the chapter you read. Using BlueLetterBible.org look up the Greek or Hebrew word and definition of one of those words.

Write your findings below:

[ ] Write down any general thoughts or questions you have as you read the chapter today.

God's Love is Unfailing: Imagine

Declaration Verse: Ruth 1:16

Remember to take a moment to "engage" as you prepare to listen: toss, catch, invite, open, expect. Invite the Words of Scripture and the Words of God to speak personally into your mind and heart.

[ ] Read Ruth 1:16

You may want to scout around in your Bible for any notes or perhaps an introduction to this book of the Bible. When using your imagination, it helps to keep in mind the context of the chapter and book that you're in. Insert yourself in the story as you ponder the following questions. Use your imagination and all your senses to be present in the scene.

[ ] When and where is this taking place? What do you imagine you might see, hear, touch, taste, or smell?

[ ] Who is speaking or writing? Whom are they addressing? Others? God? Themselves?

[ ] What are they speaking or writing about? What is their purpose?

[ ] What are the characteristics of God as shown through the Declaration Verse or chapter?

Is He steadfast, faithful, just, trustworthy, nurturing, kind, gentle, or strong? What do you see revealed about His nature in this passage of Scripture?

[ ] What are the promises of God as shown through the Declaration Verse or chapter?

Write any observations, key words, or questions you have as you ponder the Declaration Verse. If you have time, you may want to do another word study.

Digging Deeper: The Book of Ruth

[ ] Refresh your memory of Ruth Chapter 3

[ ] Imagine

> You may want flip back to the beginning of Ruth in your Bible to read the introduction. Or use on online resource. Insert yourself in the story as you ponder the following questions.
>
> When and where is this taking place? Who is speaking? What is happening?

God's Love is Unfailing: Listen

Declaration Verse: Ruth 1:16

> *Remember to take a moment to "engage" as you prepare to listen: toss, catch, invite, open, expect. Invite the Words of Scripture and the Words of God to speak personally into your mind and heart. Remember that God's voice will never accuse you. He may bring gentle conviction, and that can cause some grief, but God always brings hope.*

Listening can be pursued for several days, and in fact, God will probably speak unexpectedly at random times of day or night as His revelation is released to you. Ask these questions as you listen to God's voice:

[ ] How does the Declaration Verse apply to me?

[ ] Ponder and pray: how I can apply these truths to the frustrations, disappointments, fears, or hurts in my life? Is there anything I need to receive or surrender in my life?

Digging Deeper: The Book of Ruth

[ ] Refresh your memory of Ruth Chapter 3

[ ] Listen

Ask yourself: how does what I have read so far in Ruth Chapter 3 apply to me? Does God want to speak to my heart today through this story?

[ ] Write down any general thoughts or questions you have as you read the chapter today.

God's Love is Unfailing: Declare

Declaration Verse: Ruth 1:16

Write out a declaration of what you have received as you meditated on the Word. This can be a statement of God's promise to you, an affirmation of the healing that He has given you, or a proclamation of a truth that has become real to you. A declaration can include Scripture or your own words, or some of each.

Reflect upon your week

Write out Ruth 1:16 by hand if you memorized it, or summarize the Declaration Verse in your own words below.

Spend a few minutes documenting your insights, "a-ha" moments, and revelations from this week of digging into the Bible.

Digging Deeper: The Book of Ruth

[ ] Refresh your memory of Ruth Chapter 3

[ ] Spend a few minutes documenting your insights, "a-ha" moments, and revelations from this week of digging into Ruth.

Week Three: Discussion Topics

We provide discussion topics if you want to gather with friends to enjoy this study together. You are welcome to use these points to help guide your conversation, or you can ponder these questions as a personal reflection. Even if you are not able to meet up with a girlfriend, you're invited to join us in our private Facebook Group at facebook.com/groups/flourishgathering/

1) Do you have any thoughts or reactions to this week's devotional? Here are two passages from *A Passionate Pursuit* that may inspire an interesting conversation:

   "Difficult circumstances of life will either draw us away, like Orpah, or draw us toward God. It is the very nature of God to pursue us unfailingly with His love in all our circumstances of life."

   "The beautiful thing about surrender is that it takes only a willing heart. God's love meets us right where we are at in our faith walk. Yet, when we do surrender, even just a little part of our hearts, His love cleaves itself to us and through the transforming power of His unfailing love, we begin to change from the inside out."

2) Was there a special insight you gained from the **Investigate** practice? Perhaps an interesting word study, cross reference, or commentary?

3) What happened when you used your **Imagination**? What did you discover about the context of this chapter or book of the Bible? If you had time, did you gain insight into the character or promises of God?

4) Did God speak something special that you would like to share as you **Listened**?
5) What is your **Declaration**? How can we pray for you in this regard?
6) How about the Ruth reading plan? Anything interesting there?
7) How can we support one another this week? Prayer requests? Praise reports?

Notes

Week Four

God's Love is Unconditional

DECLARATION VERSE

"This is real love—not that we loved God, but that he loved us and sent his Son as a sacrifice to take away our sins." 1 John 4:10 (NLT)

As you enter your time of Bible Study this week, take a moment to "engage" by tuning your ears and heart to God's voice.

Toss: Throw your cares on God. Let Him bear your burdens. *Psalm 55:22*
Catch: Receive the peace that surpasses all understanding. *Philippians 4:7*
Invite: Take every thought captive. Invite clarity and focus. Refuse confusion, distraction, or double-mindedness. *2 Corinthians 10:5*
Open: Ask God if you have turned away or closed your heart to anyone. Release the offense, open your heart, and give the situation into God's care. *Psalm 139:23*
Expect: Tell God that you are looking forward to hearing from Him. Let the excitement of time in His presence build expectation in your heart. *Habakkuk 2:1*

Love Poured Out

We arrive in Judah and enter the story at another dialogue between Naomi and Ruth. This time Naomi asks Ruth to do something rather peculiar. Let's take a look:

> Naomi said to her, "My daughter, I must find a home for you, where you will be well provided for. Now Boaz, with whose women you have worked, is a relative of ours. Tonight, he will be winnowing barley on the threshing floor. Wash, put on perfume, and get dressed in your best clothes. Then go down to the threshing floor, but don't let him know you are there until he has finished eating and drinking. When he lies down, note the place where he is lying. Then go and uncover his feet and lie down. He will tell you what to do." Ruth 3:1-4 (NIV)

When I researched this unusual encounter, I discovered that Ruth's actions are seen as an act of servitude and in line with traditions during that time. Boaz knows that He is in the family line and able to "redeem" Ruth and Naomi, yet He is not sure if that is what Ruth truly desires. Historians believe that Boaz was considerably older than Ruth, so he needed confirmation before beginning the official proceedings. She is asking for his hand in marriage. *And we thought that was a modern-day thing!*

An Unlikely Redemption

This story of redemption is improbable since Ruth and Boaz are an unlikely pair, a Jew and a Gentile. The Jews are God's chosen people and worship only the one true God. Ruth on the other hand is a Gentile, born and raised in Moab, a pagan land that worships false gods and idols. This pairing is unlikely in Jewish culture. We read that when Boaz approaches the first redeemer (Ruth 4), this man is interested in redeeming the land, but he does not want the foreign woman who would have to become his wife. Matthew Henry writes:

> The land, he thought, would be an improvement of his inheritance, but not the land with the woman; that would mar it. Perhaps he thought it would be a disparagement to him to marry such a poor widow that had come from a strange

country, and almost lived upon alms. He fancied it would be a blemish to his family, it would mar his blood, and disgrace his posterity. Her eminent virtues were not sufficient in his eye to counterbalance this. (Matthew Henry Commentary on Ruth)

Ouch! Did you catch that last line? *"Her eminent virtues were not sufficient in his eye."* Thankfully, we too have an unconditional redemption available to us, and it is not conditional on our virtues. Our redemption is not based on race, gender or our past history. It is available to all of us. The story of the cross is the ultimate story of redemption, and it is centered on love at its very core.

> *This is real love—not that we loved God, but that he loved us and sent his Son as a sacrifice to take away our sins. 1 John 4:10 (NLT)*

An Unlikely Exchange

After the redemption agreement made by Boaz and the first kinsman redeemer, I noticed an interesting exchange:

> *Now was the custom in former times in Israel concerning redeeming and exchanging: to confirm a transaction, the one drew off his sandal and gave it to the other; and this was the manner of attesting in Israel. Ruth 4:7 (NIV)*

I was fascinated by this quirky and odd custom, then it hit me. We too are *"exchanged."* When Jesus died on the cross he gave his very life in **exchange** for our sins. All our sins. And when we receive Jesus into our hearts, we **exchange** our old sin nature for our new identity in Christ.

Several years ago, I was invited to speak at a women's retreat. As I arrived that weekend, I laid my heart's requests before the Lord, and I thought I knew exactly how He would answer to me. One of the other speakers was a mighty prayer warrior, and I was eager to get a few minutes of her time so that she could pray over me in an area of my life where I felt stuck. The weekend came and went, and when our last morning arrived, I had yet to be able to pray with her. I was devastated and thought I would be leaving without the healing I desired.

That morning each of the participants was asked to write a word on a stone that represented their weekend. For some reason I chose the phrase "new creation." I quickly scribbled the phrase and glanced over my speaking notes as I was to speak right after the worship set. During worship, the prayer warrior I so desperately wanted to speak with came over and whispered in my ear: *"Jenny, the Lord wants me to tell you that you are a new creation and those very areas that you desired to be healed are being made new at this very moment."*

I couldn't believe it! That is the exact phrase the Lord had spoken to me. I was reminded that the unconditional love of God through the sacrifice of Jesus exchanged my old self with all my brokenness and gave me a new identity, therefore making me a new creation: *"Therefore, if anyone is in Christ, the new creation has come: The old has gone, the new is here!" 2 Corinthians 5:17 (NIV)*

A Love Story Unfolding

The greatest love story, the story of God's love for His people continues to play out in the lives of the least likely, the forgotten, and the sinner. Stories like that of Naomi and Ruth remind us that God's unconditional love passionately pursues us on purpose. And there is always a purpose, as God desires to abundantly bless us beyond our wildest imagination (Ephesians 3:20). Ruth would go on to marry Boaz and give birth to a son that would become the grandfather to King David. Their family was now grafted into the lineage of Jesus. What an honor!

Our lives in the hands of God's love are redeemed. We are a new creation, no longer defined or limited by our past, our sin, or our failure. Because of the Lord's unconditional love that paid the final price for our sin, once and for all, Jesus shed His blood as an act of dedicated sacrifice for you and for me.

When we acknowledge God's love, believe in His love, and surrender our hearts to His love, we receive God's gift of redemption through Jesus Christ.

This is the greatest love story ever told!

God's Love is Unconditional: Read & Write

Declaration Verse: 1 John 4:10

"This is real love—not that we loved God, but that he loved us and sent his Son as a sacrifice to take away our sins." 1 John 4:10

[ ] Read 1 John 4:10 slowly once or twice, even out loud if you are able.

[ ] Write 1 John 4:9-11 in the space below. *Feel free to get creative!*

[ ] Read 1 John Chapter 4 for context. Write out a few observations:

[ ] Read 1 John 4:10 in another Bible translation. Do you notice any differences?

Write your observations

Digging Deeper: The Book of Ruth

[ ] Read Ruth Chapter 4

[ ] Write any verses that stand out to you as you read the chapter.

God's Love is Unconditional: Investigate

Declaration Verse: 1 John 4:10

Today we begin looking deeper into the Declaration Verse. Investigate as little or as much as time allows. Online resources like BibleGateway.com or BlueLetterBible.org will help you during your investigation.

[ ] Conduct a Word Study: Part One

Read the Declaration Verse or the entire chapter if you have more time. Spend a few minutes highlighting any words you want to research more.

Write these words below:

[ ] Conduct a Word Study: Part Two

Using BlueLetterBible.org or another online resource, choose a word you selected above to conduct your word study. This is as simple as looking up the original Greek or Hebrew word, reading the definitions of that word, and looking at how it is used in other verses in the Bible.

Record the results of your word study here:

[ ] Read any of the following cross references for 1 John 4:10:

   2 Corinthians 5:19
   John 1:14
   Isaiah 44:22

   Reading cross references will help you better understand a verse, word, or principle.

   What did you discover? Write your insights:

[ ] Read a commentary. A commentary is a collection of explanatory notes that a Bible scholar has written about passages of scripture. Write any observations, quotes, or notes:

Digging Deeper: The Book of Ruth

[ ] Refresh your memory of Ruth Chapter 4

[ ] Investigate

Highlight a couple key words that stand out to you in the chapter you read. Using BlueLetterBible.org look up the Greek or Hebrew word and definition of one of those words.

Write your findings below:

[ ] Write down any general thoughts or questions you have as you read the chapter today.

God's Love is Unconditional: Imagine

Declaration Verse: 1 John 4:10

> *Remember to take a moment to "engage" as you prepare to listen: toss, catch, invite, open, expect. Invite the Words of Scripture and the Words of God to speak personally into your mind and heart.*

[ ] Read 1 John 4:10

You may want to scout around in your Bible for any notes or perhaps an introduction to this book of the Bible. When using your imagination, it helps to keep in mind the context of the chapter and book that you're in. Insert yourself in the story as you ponder the following questions. Use your imagination and all your senses to be present in the scene.

[ ] When and where is this taking place? What do you imagine you might see, hear, touch, taste, or smell?

[ ] Who is speaking or writing? Whom are they addressing? Others? God?
Themselves?

[ ] What are they speaking or writing about? What is their purpose?

[ ] What are the characteristics of God as shown through the Declaration Verse or chapter?

Is He steadfast, faithful, just, trustworthy, nurturing, kind, gentle, or strong? What do you see revealed about His nature in this passage of Scripture?

[ ] What are the promises of God as shown through the Declaration Verse or chapter?

Write any observations, key words, or questions you have as you ponder the Declaration Verse. If you have time, you may want to do another word study.

Digging Deeper: The Book of Ruth

[ ] Refresh your memory of Ruth Chapter 4

[ ] Imagine

> You may want flip back to the beginning of Ruth in your Bible to read the introduction. Or use on online resource. Insert yourself in the story as you ponder the following questions.

> When and where is this taking place? Who is speaking? What is happening?

God's Love is Unconditional: Listen

Declaration Verse: 1 John 4:10

> *Remember to take a moment to "engage" as you prepare to listen: toss, catch, invite, open, expect. Invite the Words of Scripture and the Words of God to speak personally into your mind and heart. Remember that God's voice will never accuse you. He may bring gentle conviction, and that can cause some grief, but God always brings hope.*

Listening can be pursued for several days, and in fact, God will probably speak unexpectedly at random times of day or night as His revelation is released to you. Ask these questions as you listen to God's voice:

[ ] How does the Declaration Verse apply to me?

[ ] Ponder and pray: how I can apply these truths to the frustrations, disappointments, fears, or hurts in my life? Is there anything I need to receive or surrender in my life?

Digging Deeper: The Book of Ruth

[ ] Refresh your memory of Ruth Chapter 4

[ ] Listen

> Ask yourself: how does what I have read so far in Ruth Chapter 4 apply to me? Does God want to speak to my heart today through this story?

[ ] Write down any general thoughts or questions you have as you read the chapter today.

God's Love is Unconditional: Declare

Declaration Verse: 1 John 4:10

Write out a declaration of what you have received as you meditated on the Word. This can be a statement of God's promise to you, an affirmation of the healing that He has given you, or a proclamation of a truth that has become real to you. A declaration can include Scripture or your own words, or some of each.

Reflect upon your week

Write out 1 John 4:10 by hand if you memorized it, or summarize the Declaration Verse in your own words below.

Spend a few minutes documenting your insights, "a-ha" moments, and revelations from this week of digging into the Bible.

Digging Deeper: The Book of Ruth

[ ] Refresh your memory of Ruth Chapter 4

[ ] Spend a few minutes documenting your insights, "a-ha" moments, and
   revelations from this week of digging into Ruth.

Week Four: Discussion Topics

We provide discussion topics if you want to gather with friends to enjoy this study together. You are welcome to use these points to help guide your conversation, or you can ponder these questions as a personal reflection. Even if you are not able to meet up with a girlfriend, you're invited to join us in our private Facebook Group at facebook.com/groups/flourishgathering/

1) Do you have any thoughts or reactions to this week's devotional? Here are two passages from *Love Poured Out* that may inspire an interesting conversation:

   "Thankfully, we too have an unconditional redemption available to us, and it is not conditional on our virtues. Our redemption is not based on race, gender or our past history. It is available to all of us. The story of the cross is the ultimate story of redemption, and it is centered on love at its very core."

   "Our lives in the hands of God's love are redeemed. We are a new creation, no longer defined or limited by our past, our sin, or our failure. Because of the Lord's unconditional love that paid the final price for our sin, once and for all, Jesus shed His blood as an act of dedicated sacrifice for you and for me."

2) Was there a special insight you gained from the **Investigate** practice? Perhaps an interesting word study, cross reference, or commentary?

3) What happened when you used your **Imagination**? What did you discover about the context of this chapter or book of the Bible? If you had time, did you gain insight into the character or promises of God?

4) Did God speak something special that you would like to share as you **Listened**?

5) What is your **Declaration**? How can we pray for you in this regard?

6) How about the Ruth reading plan? Anything interesting there?

7) How can we support one another this week? Prayer requests? Praise reports?

Notes

The Love of the Father

We have a bittersweet feeling as the conclusion of a Flourish Study approaches. In God's great kindness, He creates this space and invites us to enjoy time with Him in the pages of this journal and in our community of women. He is present in the midst of our devotion. He speaks into our lives and fills up our hearts with His love. The great Yahweh, whose holy name is the very breath in our bodies, considers it pure joy to spend time with His daughters. Lavishing love on us is one of His greatest pleasures:

> See what great love the Father has lavished on us, that we should be called children of God! And that is what we are! 1 John 3:1 (NIV)

Here in First John, the "disciple whom Jesus loved" pauses to reflect upon his life journey. He is well-qualified to speak on the subject of the Christ, having walked closely with Jesus during His three years of public ministry. John, his brother James, and Peter prayed with the Messiah (and fell asleep!) in the garden of Gethsemane the night their Rabbi was betrayed and handed over to be crucified (Matthew 26). This is the beloved disciple whom Jesus asked to care for his mother, Mary, as He neared death on the cross (John 19:27). We can reasonably assume that when John reflects upon his life of faith, his insights will be of great import to us.

What does this faithful disciple choose to emphasize in his reflections of a life lived in service to God? Love! He arrives at old age, a revered and esteemed elder statesman of the church, and his language is full of gratitude and humility for God as a Father who invites us to be His children.

Why is it important to know God as Father?

I had an interesting conversation with a wise man of God who spent many years of his life teaching about The Father's Love. Jack Frost, of Shiloh Place Ministries, traveled the world in fulfilment of his calling to invite all people to experience the embrace of the Father. He discovered as he did so, that many of us have some difficulty with how we view the Trinity: God as Father, Son, and Spirit.

In our confusion, we can be tempted to believe that a loving Jesus came to save us from an angry, cruel God. This assumption will affect the way we encounter God's love, creating doubt about the love of the Father. Add to this the father and mother wounds that most of us suffer in childhood, and it is no wonder that we may be leery of parental love coming from an Abba Daddy God whose goodness is doubtful.

At some stage, God invites each of us to allow Him to rewrite the story of broken love that is the result of life in this fallen world. When we surrender to God's love, we position ourselves as His children to receive His gentle affection and His unwavering devotion that is the full expression of His nature in three Persons: Father, Son, and Spirit.

The generous redemptive love that Boaz shows to Ruth and Naomi is a picture of the unfailing love that God wishes to lavish upon to us. We pray that you will let Him deeper into your heart, that you will yield to His wooing. He is good. He is trustworthy. May you fully receive the story of love that He wishes to write upon your life.

We have included **The Father's Love Letter,** written as an intimate message from God to you. Allow these paraphrased words of Scripture to open your heart to Father:

My Child,

You may not know me, but I know everything about you. Psalm 139:1 *I know when you sit down and when you rise up.* Psalm 139:2 *I am familiar with all your ways.* Psalm 139:3 *Even the very hairs on your head are numbered.* Matthew 10:29-31 *For you were made in my image.* Genesis 1:27 *In me you live and move and have your being.* Acts 17:28 *For you are my offspring.* Acts 17:28 *I knew you even before you were conceived.* Jeremiah 1:4-5 *I chose you when I planned creation.* Ephesians 1:11-12 *You were not a mistake, for all your days are written in my book.* Psalm 139:15-16 *I determined the exact time of your birth and where you would live.* Acts 17:26 *You are fearfully and wonderfully made.* Psalm 139:14 *I knit you together in your mother's womb.* Psalm 139:13 *And brought you forth on the day you were born.* Psalm 71:6

I have been misrepresented by those who don't know me. John 8:41-44 *I am not distant and angry, but am the complete expression of love.* 1 John 4:16 *And it is my desire to lavish my love on you.* 1 John 3:1 *Simply because you are my child and I am your Father.* 1 John 3:1 *I offer you more than your earthly father ever could.* Matthew 7:11 *For I am the perfect father.* Matthew 5:48 *Every good gift that you receive comes from my hand.* James 1:17 *For I am your provider and I meet all your needs.* Matthew 6:31-33 *My plan for*

perfect father. Matthew 5:48 *Every good gift that you receive comes from my hand.* James 1:17 *For I am your provider and I meet all your needs.* Matthew 6:31-33 *My plan for your future has always been filled with hope.* Jeremiah 29:11 *Because I love you with an everlasting love.* Jeremiah 31:3 *My thoughts toward you are countless as the sand on the seashore.* Psalm 139:17-18 *And I rejoice over you with singing.* Zephaniah 3:17

I will never stop doing good to you. Jeremiah 32:40 *For you are my treasured possession.* Exodus 19:5 *I desire to establish you with all my heart and all my soul.* Jeremiah 32:41 *And I want to show you great and marvelous things.* Jeremiah 33:3 *If you seek me with all your heart, you will find me.* Deuteronomy 4:29 *Delight in me and I will give you the desires of your heart.* Psalm 37:4 *For it is I who gave you those desires.* Philippians 2:13 *I am able to do more for you than you could possibly imagine.* Ephesians 3:20 *For I am your greatest encourager.* 2 Thessalonians 2:16-17

I am also the Father who comforts you in all your troubles. 2 Corinthians 1:3-4 *When you are brokenhearted, I am close to you.* Psalm 34:18 *As a shepherd carries a lamb, I have carried you close to my heart.* Isaiah 40:11 *One day I will wipe away every tear from your eyes.* Revelation 21:3-4 *And I'll take away all the pain you have suffered on this earth.* Revelation 21:3-4

I am your Father, and I love you even as I love my son, Jesus. John 17:23 *For in Jesus, my love for you is revealed.* John 17:26 *He is the exact representation of my being.* Hebrews 1:3 *He came to demonstrate that I am for you, not against you.* Romans 8:31 *And to tell you that I am not counting your sins.* 2 Corinthians 5:18-19 *Jesus died so that you and I could be reconciled.* 2 Corinthians 5:18-19 *His death was the ultimate expression of my love for you.* 1 John 4:10 *I gave up everything I loved that I might gain your love.* Romans 8:31-32

If you receive the gift of my son Jesus, you receive me. 1 John 2:23 *And nothing will ever separate you from my love again.* Romans 8:38-39 *Come home and I'll throw the biggest party heaven has ever seen.* Luke 15:7 *I have always been Father, and will always be Father.* Ephesians 3:14-15

My question is... Will you be my child? John 1:12-13

Love, Your Dad, Almighty God

A Note to Group Leaders

We are pleased that you have chosen to gather a group of ladies to enjoy this Flourish Bible Study together. The study is designed to create deep, thoughtful conversations. Chatting through the insights gained using the five simple DECLARE practices each week will guide the discussion to reveal personal "a-ha's" that come straight from Scripture. It is motivating and encouraging when ladies share how God speaks in their lives.

We have provided here a few considerations regarding scheduling:
- Since it is a four-week study, you have several choices for your meeting schedule. You can meet up weekly for four weeks, or maybe you meet only twice and cover two weeks at a time. Most groups enjoy 1-1/2 or 2 hours together.
- Some groups like to add a fifth meeting time to gather before the study begins to hand out the books and view the first video. See below for suggestions in the use of the video resources.

The (Deeper) Flourish Experience resources are provided to enhance your gathering:
- The **Weekly Teaching Videos** provide approximately 15-18 minutes of content, including a small group discussion and teaching from Jenny or Mindy.
- This weekly video can be shown at the beginning of your meeting time, or at the end. Alternatively, you can assign the video material for women to watch at home before they come.
- You may also choose to show **The Redemption Series** videos, or these also can be viewed at home. These stories may be used as conversation starters.

We suggest that you make use of the weekly **Discussion Topics** located at the end of each week to facilitate the discussion. Most facilitators like to use this guide as a building block to create a general time schedule for your meeting. You may want to reserve fifteen minutes or so at the end of your group time to share prayer requests.

Gathering women to share their stories invites God's love to shine: *"They triumphed over him by the blood of the Lamb and by the word of their testimony." (Revelation 12:11)* We pray that you are blessed as you flourish together!

A little bit about Flourish

Flourish is a gathering of women who passionately pursue God and His Word. We encourage one another through genuine, transparent relationships which equip us to thrive where we are planted and impact our world for the glory of God.

We believe that the power of God's Word revealed by the Spirit changes lives. In relationship with God and with one another, we are strengthened to overcome hindrances in our journey. Flourish is dedicated to bringing God's Word to life in the 21st Century by encouraging women that the Word is alive, active, and powerful today.

Now here's our purpose spelled out in regular talk.

We want more of God, so we dig into His Word. We can't survive without Him. We can't survive without you either. You can leave your mask at the door because real life is messy, and no one here is pretending to have it all together

At Flourish we…

ENCOURAGE

We share real stories of real life with transparency and honesty, always pointing to the promises found in God's Word.

EQUIP

Flourish provides tools and resources that are grounded in the Word of God. Our community provides a safe place to learn and to grow.

ACTIVATE

We seek God in community because, when the rubber hits the road, we want to see evidence of God's life in our relationships.

About the Authors

Meet Mindy . . .

Mindy Kiker is a committed Floridian, enjoying a quiet woodland home that she and her husband built to shelter their four boisterous boys. Born in Tucson, Arizona, Mindy's magical childhood included a four-year hiatus on the big island of Hawaii where she danced the hula, and later helped with the family marina in Cedar Key where she learned to cast net and sail the Gulf of Mexico. The Kikers spent the 1990s in South Africa, returning with their brood for a sabbatical year in 2012 to reconnect with beloved friends and favorite places.

Now that Mindy's spring-chicken days are drawing to a close, she has accepted her role as an "older" woman (it's all relative) cheering others on in life's journey. A favorite verse that motivates her to keep pressing into God and encouraging her friends to do the same is *Galatians 5:1, "It is for freedom that Christ has set us free. Stand firm, then, and do not let yourselves be burdened again by a yoke of slavery."*

And Jenny . . .

Jenny Kochert was born and raised in sunny South Florida. Although she took full advantage of big-city life growing up, she longed to move to a quieter town, and college provided the perfect excuse! After graduating from the University of Florida, Jenny followed in the family footsteps and became a private investigator (yes, you read that right!), opening her own agency in 2005.

However, once she became a mom to her daughter, Sophia, she turned in her badge, and settled at home, now home schooling her daughter. Jenny, her husband Ryan, and daughter Sophia now live in Northern Kentucky where they serve in ministry together as a family. God has put a story on her lips and a passion in her heart to encourage women, and she is thrilled that she gets to do that each and every day.

Thank you

for joining us for His **Love** Is

Connect with us on Facebook:
@Flourishgathering

Contact us:
info@flourishgathering.com

Visit us:
Flourishgathering.com

Made in the USA
Lexington, KY
15 February 2018